I spy with my little eye...

EDWARD GIBBS

B||F| & |F

BRUBAKER, FORD & FRIENDS

AN IMPRINT OF THE TEMPLAR COMPANY LIMITED

I spy with my little eye…

something
that is **blue**.

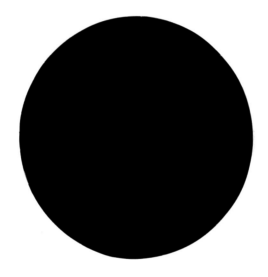

I am the
biggest animal in
the whole world.

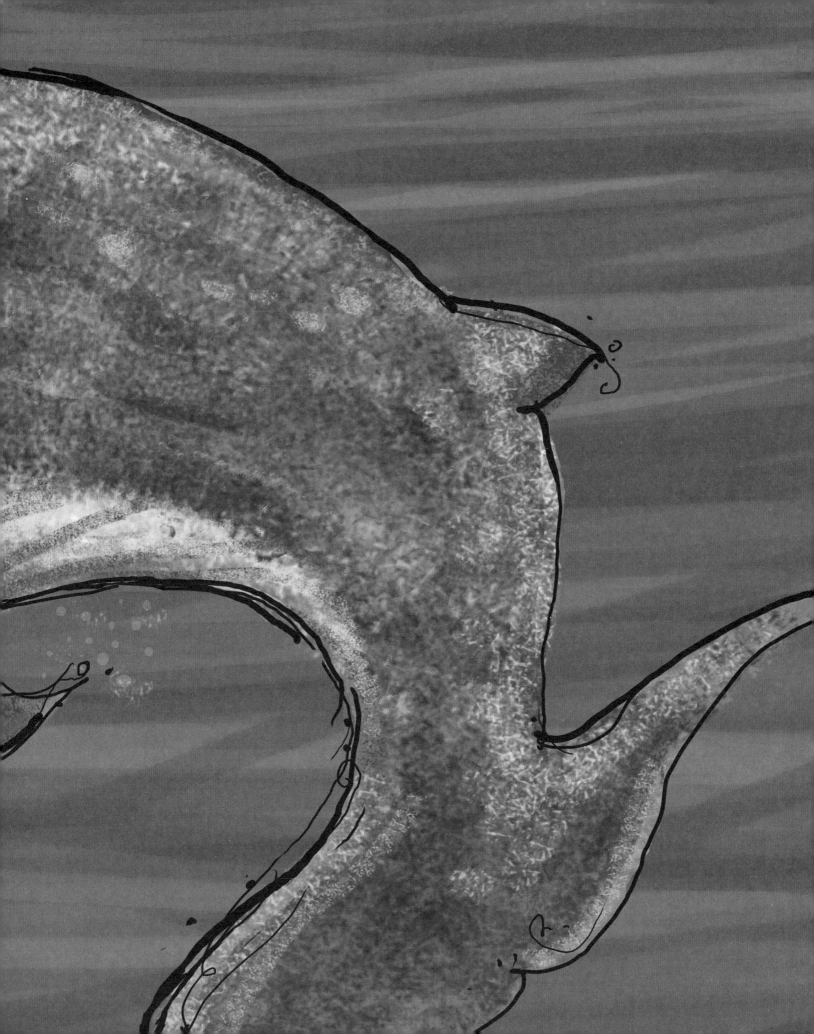

I spy with my little eye...

something
that is **grey**.

I have a very
long trunk.

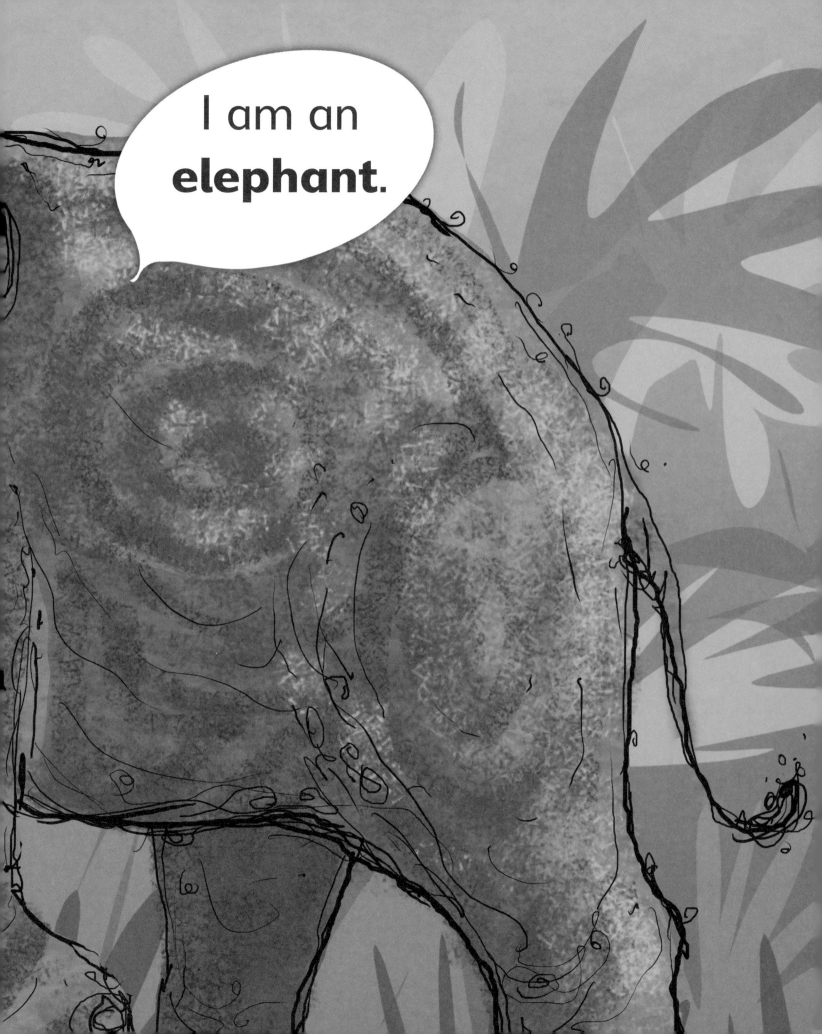

I spy with my little eye...

something
that is **white**.

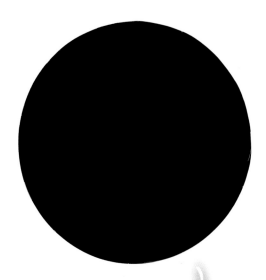

The North Pole
is my home.

I spy with my little eye...

something
that is **yellow**.

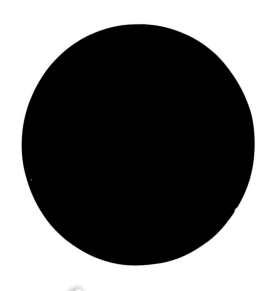

I am the king
of the jungle —
hear me ROAR!

I spy with my little eye...

something
that is **orange**.

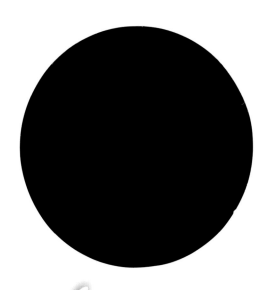

I swing
from tree to
tree with my
long arms.

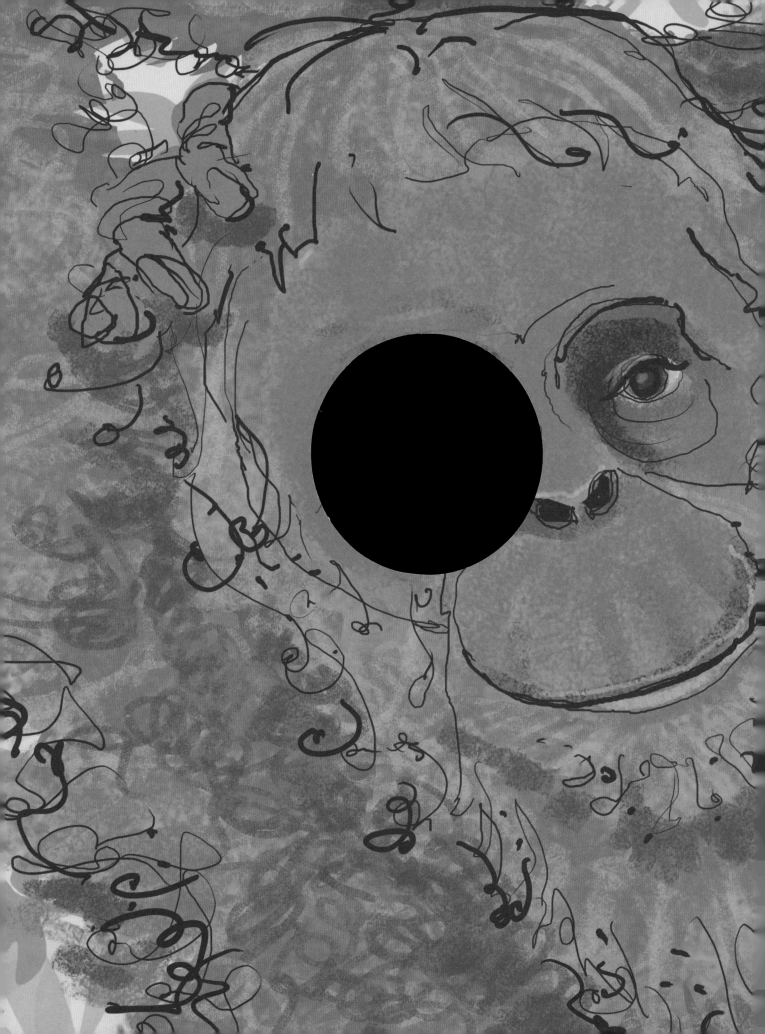

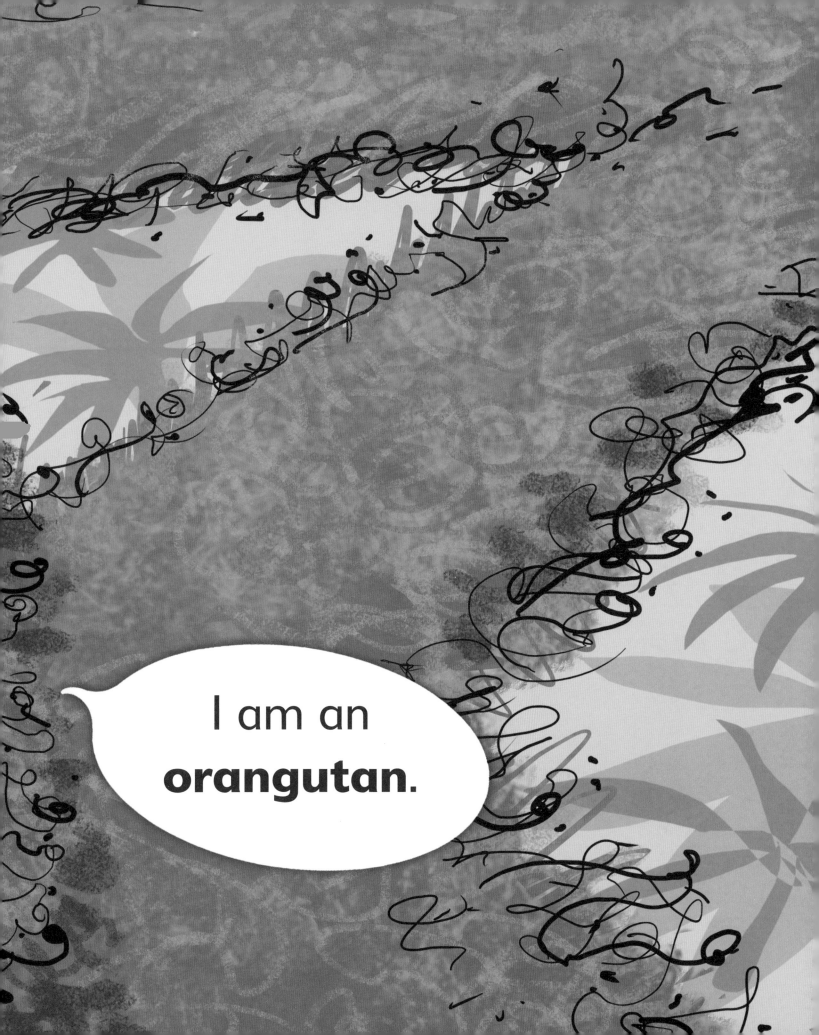

I spy with my little eye...

something
that is **red**.

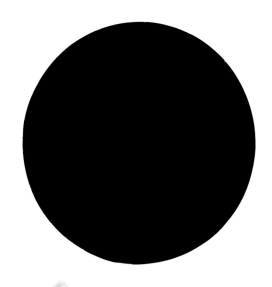

I have
a long
bushy tail.

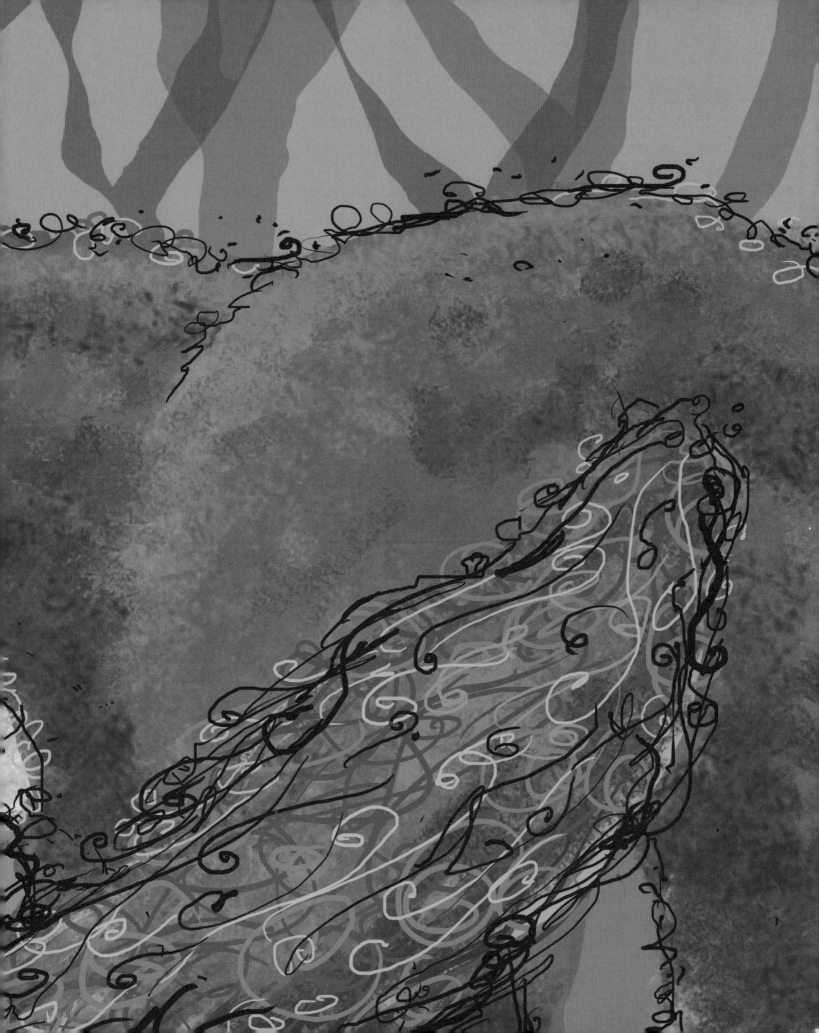

I spy with my little eye...

something that is **green**.

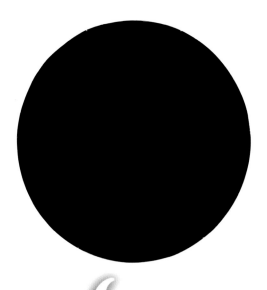

I hop about on my long legs.